SHORT FUSE

LILI RISTAGNO

DYMAXICON

Published by Dymaxicon
An imprint of Agile Learning Labs
San Francisco, CA

second edition
ISBN 978-0-9828669-4-8

www.dymaxicon.com

edited by Nancy Rommelmann
layout by Hillary Louise Johnson
text set in Set Fire To the Rain
title text set in Base 2 & Ed Gein

Originally published in a limited edition by the author.

SHORT FUSE

A GRAPHIC NOVEL BY

LILI RISTAGNO

THIS IS A TRUE STORY

Nebraska is a place of endless horizon and enormous sky. Summers are long days of fierce light, hot winds and palpable humidity.

Everything hatches or buds at an accelerated rate and expires just as quickly, spent from the heat. Dead things are everywhere.

To stand outside in winter is to feel the force of a gathered ferocity, bent on freezing and flattening everything in its path.

During the winter, too, everything dies. Icy winds gain strength, pushed across a thousand miles of prairie.

A peculiar form of claustrophobia sets in when one is surrounded by nothing. The horizon mocks, always hopelessly distant. It is easy to see that there is truly nowhere to go.

This is the story of a boy trapped by space, the story of a killer. It is also a love story.

the plains
a flat arithmetic
of space

Caril Fugate was in the eighth grade.

Charlie Starkweather was 19.

He loved the feeling of the gun in his hands,
In spite of his poor eyesight, he was
an excellent shot. It was important
the animals not suffer.
A 9th grade dropout, Charlie was good at souping up hot rods and hunting.
SPORTS
Charlie's father was a taciturn man, ruling the household with an iron hand, or, if he was drinking, an iron fist. In October of 1957, Guy Starkweather threw Charlie out of the house.

Caril was thirteen. She lived with her mother, stepfather, and half-sister Betty-Jean. Their home was a tiny clap-board house without indoor plumbing in the poorest section of town.

Caril did badly in school. She had been outside the city limits once in her life, to a nearby campground.

Caril's older sister was dating Charlie's best friend. One night they all went to the drive-in.

Charlie was impressed with Caril, who smoked, cursed and had the figure of a much older girl.

She liked to wear blue jeans and white majorette boots.

He met her every day when she got out of school, and fixed up a car for her to drive herself when he couldn't be there.

Charlie's daredevil reputation followed him to the track. Looking at Caril on the sidelines, he wanted to become a hero for this girl.

Charlie worked as a
garbage man in the
morning, making money
to spend on Caril and
on cars. Laboring in
wealthy neighborhoods,
he grew resentful.

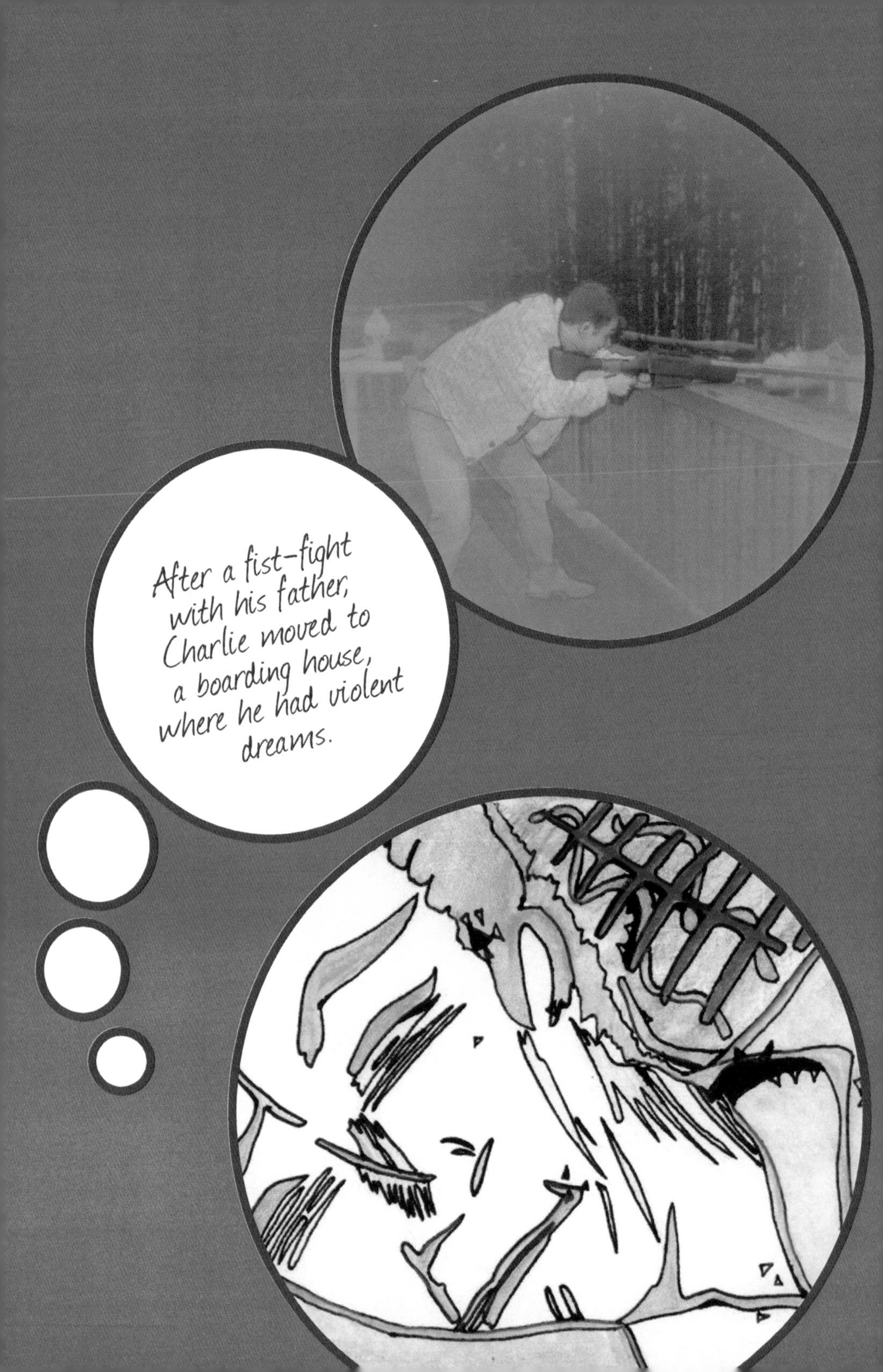
After a fist-fight
with his father,
Charlie moved to
a boarding house,
where he had violent
dreams.

Showing him his coffin, Charlie's visitor told him his time would soon come, and bade him to be patient. Charlie always promised he would try.

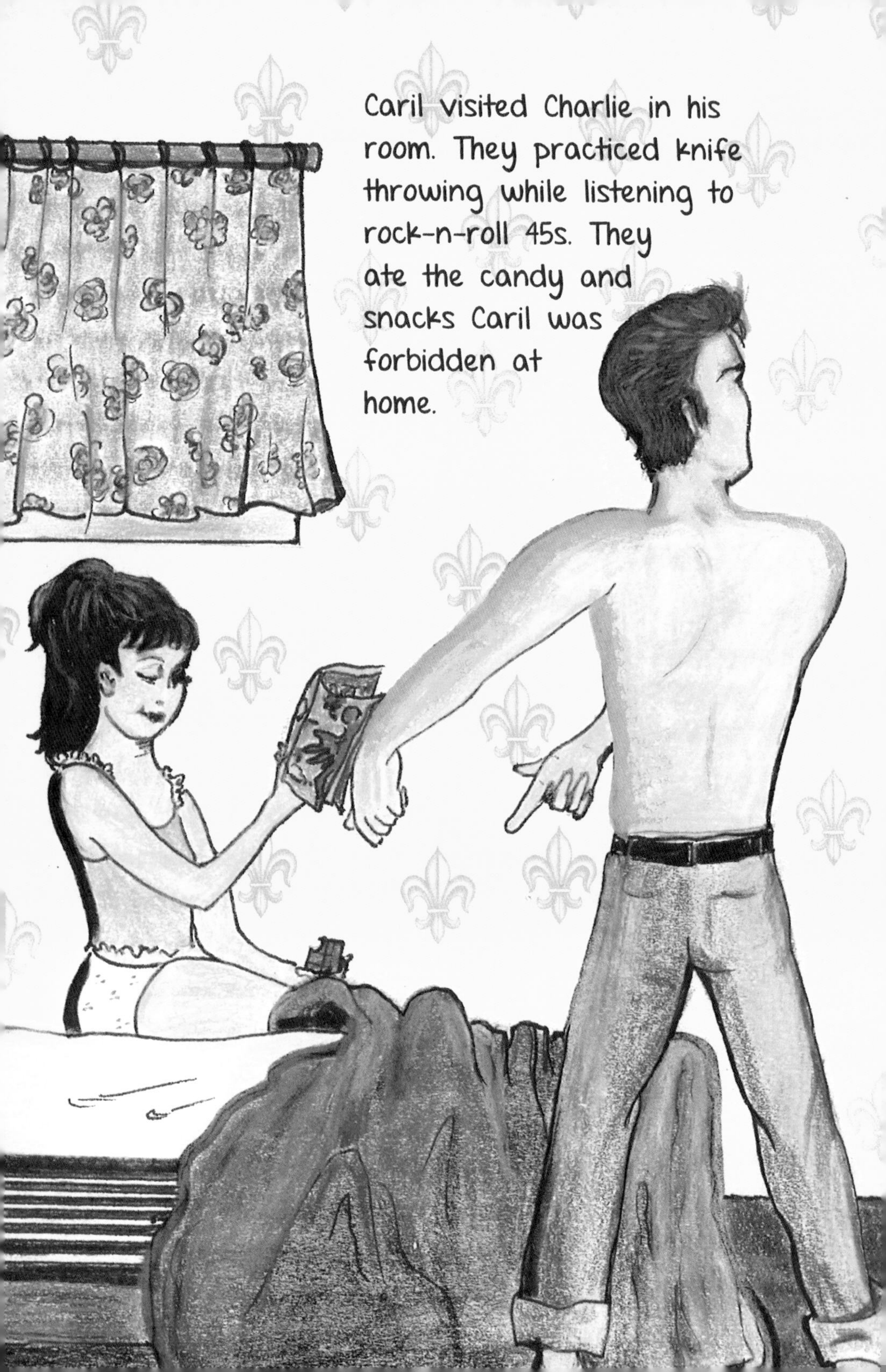
Caril visited Charlie in his
room. They practiced knife
throwing while listening to
rock-n-roll 45s. They
ate the candy and
snacks Caril was
forbidden at
home.

Robert Colvert was twenty-one and working at the Crest gas station when Charlie showed up one late December night.

Taking $108 from the cash register, Charlie forced the young man to drive out to a field, where he shot and killed him.

Caril's family
thought Charlie
was going nowhere fast,
but she told him she loved "every hair on his head." He trusted in her love. He knew, he said, that "this girl wouldn't be putting out to some other guy the next night."

She gave him a reason to live, if only long enough to tell the world to go to hell.

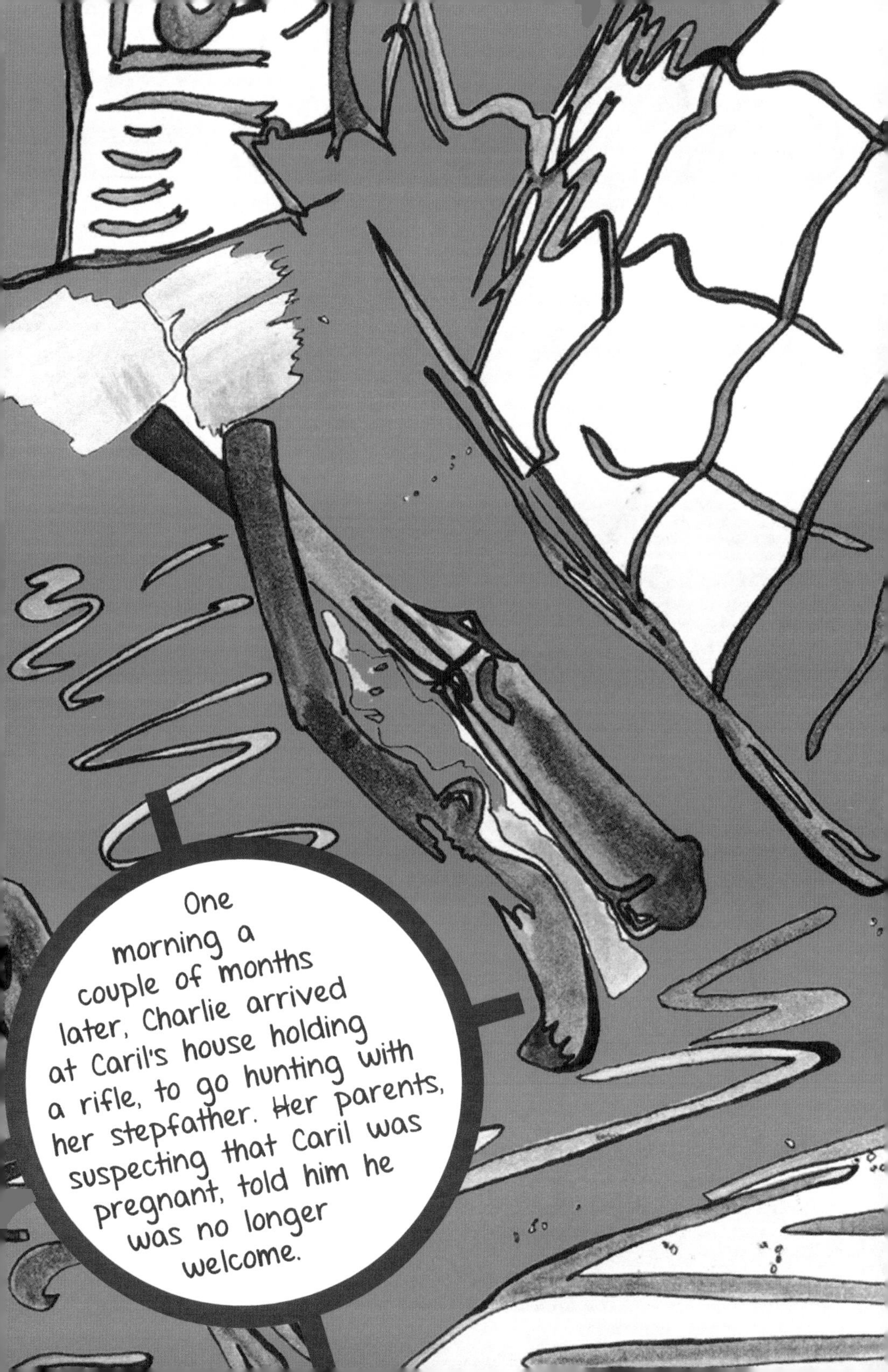
One morning a couple of months later, Charlie arrived at Caril's house holding a rifle, to go hunting with her stepfather. Her parents, suspecting that Caril was pregnant, told him he was no longer welcome.

Charlie shot Caril's parents dead and threw a knife at Betty-Jean, killing her as well.

STAY AWAY
EVERY
Body is
sick with
The FLUE
Caril wrote a note and stuck it on the screen door to keep visitors away.

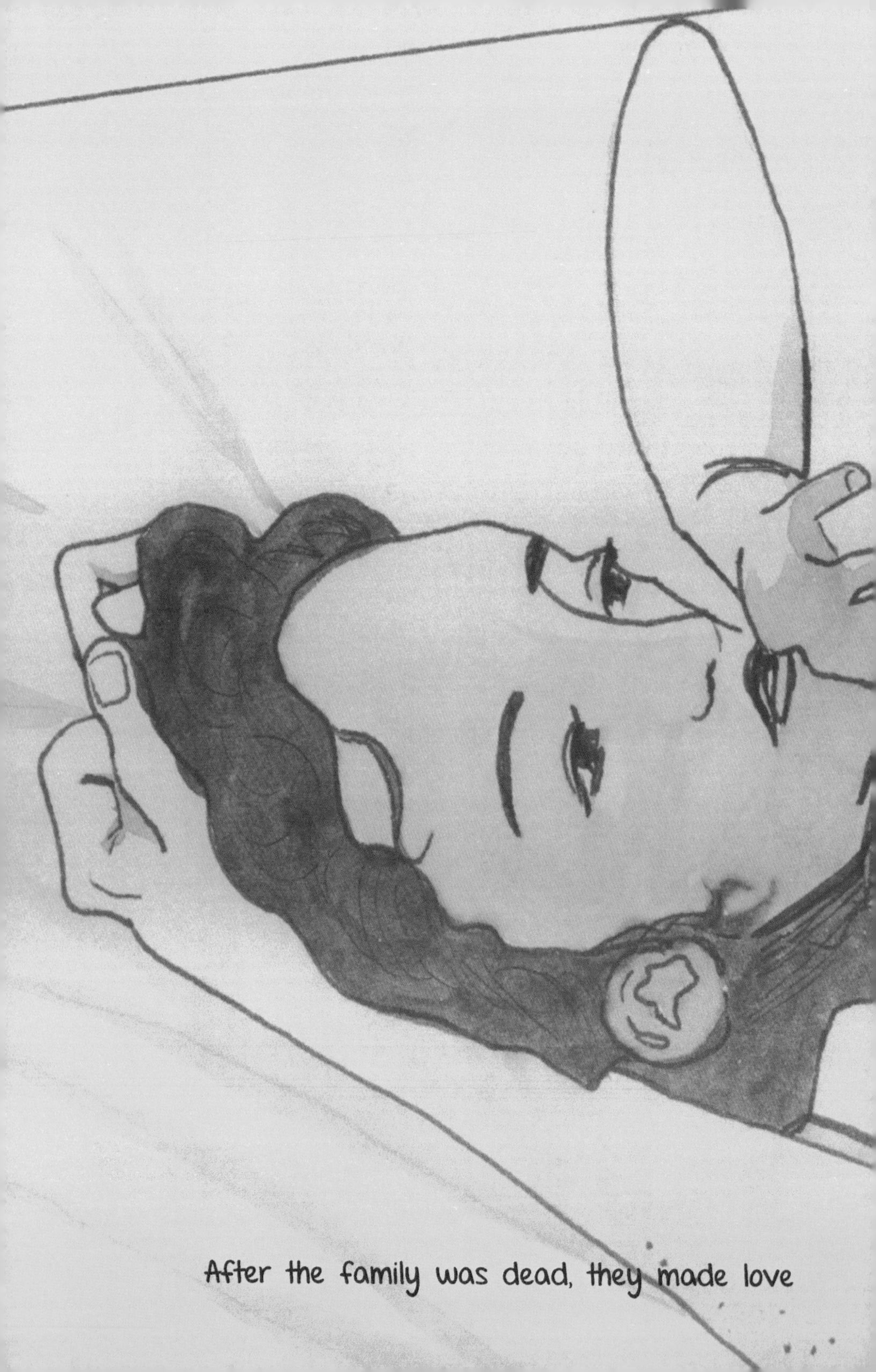
After the family was dead, they made love

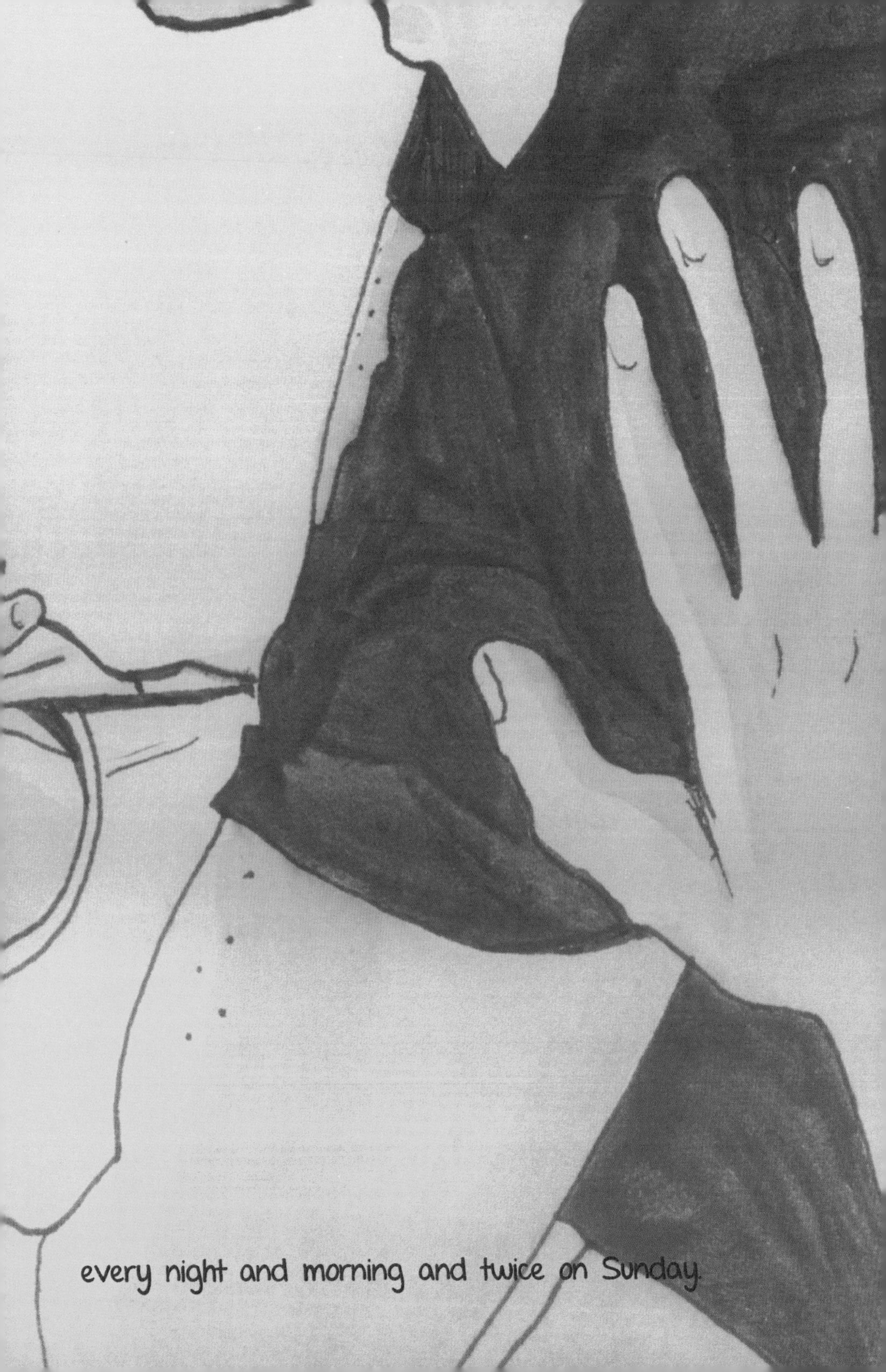
every night and morning and twice on Sunday.

For the next six days, they lived as they pleased, dining on soda and candy and watching TV. When relatives stopped by, Caril turned them away. Concerned, they asked the police to visit. The officers saw nothing amiss.

Caril never attempted to escape.

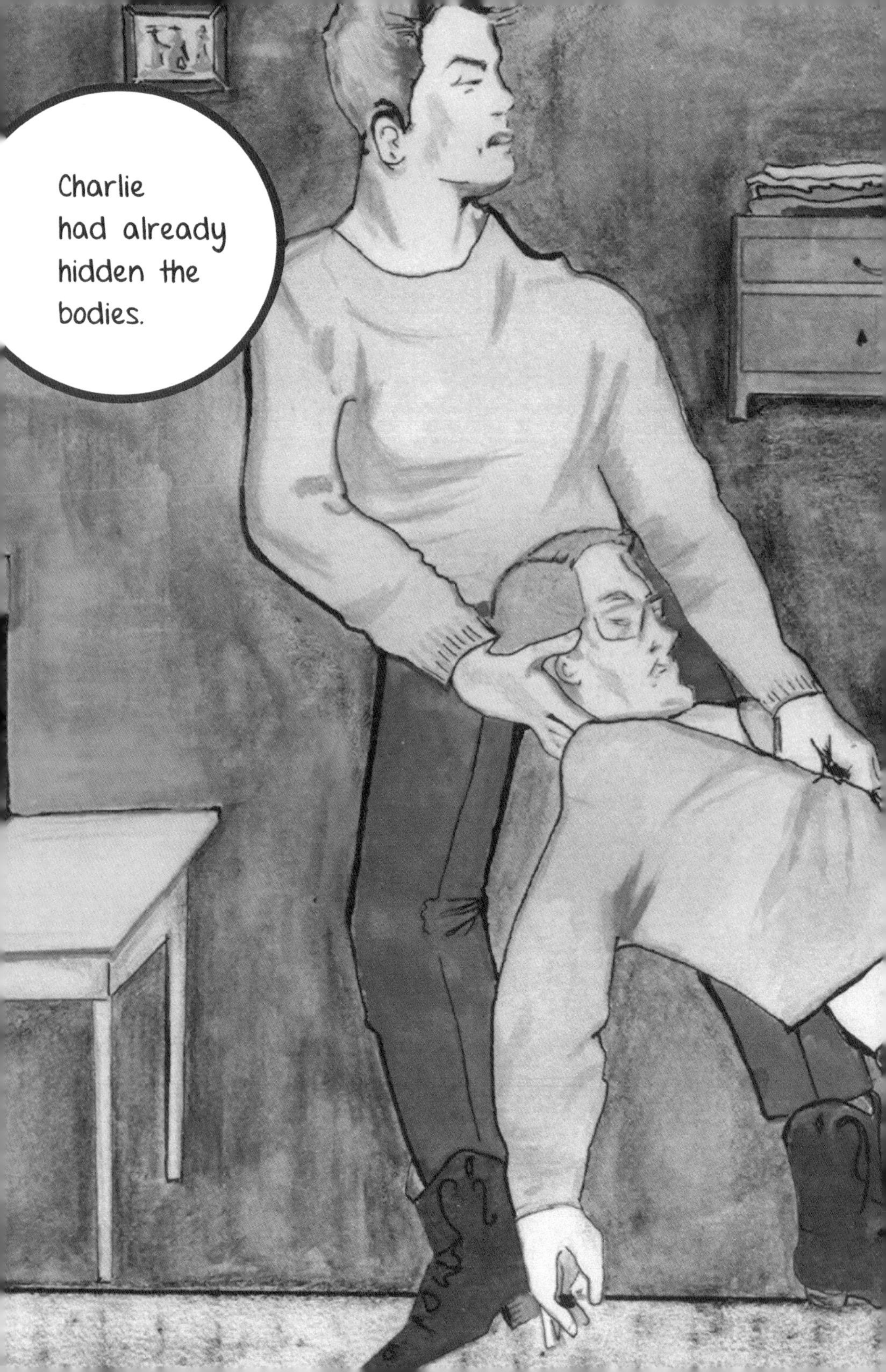
Charlie had already hidden the bodies.

Charlie and Caril left on the seventh morning, heading out to the Nebraska countryside to visit Charlie's friend, the farmer.

The family was later found bundled up in throw-rugs and frozen - two in the outhouse, one in the chicken coop.

The car got
stuck in the mud
of the farmer's lane.
They started walking.

They were so cold by the time they reached the farmhouse that Charlie shot the farmer dead.

Inside the house,
they looked for food
and money, took a
nap, and found some
rifles.

They headed back
toward the highway.

Robert Jensen and Carol King were "A" students and high school sweethearts who lived in nearby Bennet.

They were out on a date when they saw a couple by the side of the road and stopped to give them a lift.

Holding them at gunpoint, Charlie took the wheel.
They were forced into the back seat, where Caril demanded their wallets.

The authorities were one day behind the outlaw couple. They found the victims in a tornado cellar the next afternoon.

Bob Jensen had been shot while descending the steps to join Carol King. Carol had already been killed, as well as sexually attacked with a sharp instrument. Who assaulted her has never been established.

With the money from the hold-up they headed back toward Lincoln, stopping on the way to get burgers. Later the waitress recalled that Caril looked at her strangely, but said nothing after giving her the order.

They slept in the car

until past dawn....

C. Lauer Ward and his wife were a wealthy couple. He was an influential industrialist, and she was involved in social events and charities.
Lillian Fencl, the Wards' deaf housekeeper, had been with them for 26 years and was considered a member of the family.

Charlie and Caril
watched Mr. Ward
leave his mansion in
the morning...
They slipped
in the back
door, unnoticed
by the maid.

Charlie ordered Mrs. Ward to serve him pancakes in the library, then changed his order to waffles...

For a few hours Charlie and Caril enjoyed the luxurious surroundings while holding the two women hostage.

Mrs. Ward attempted to escape in the afternoon. Charlie threw a knife into her back as she ran.

Mr. Ward returned home from work early in the evening and was shot after a struggle.

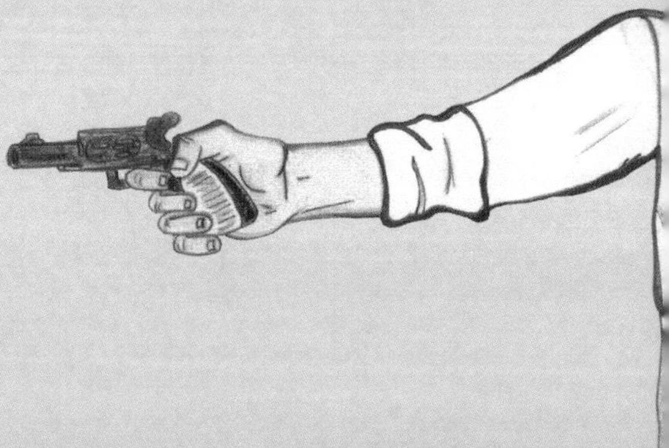

Both teenagers would later note that they "thought the maid would never die."

In the Wards' elegant car, they again pressed north... this time headed for Washington state.
Charlie had Caril throw the kitchen knife out the car window.

Broadcasts on the radio warned of the dangerous fugitives. The National Guard had by then been summoned to protect the citizens of Lincoln.

Crossing into Wyoming the next day, they saw a car by the side of the road. A travelling salesman was asleep in it...

He refused to trade cars with them.

While Charlie wrestled to pull his body from the driver's seat...

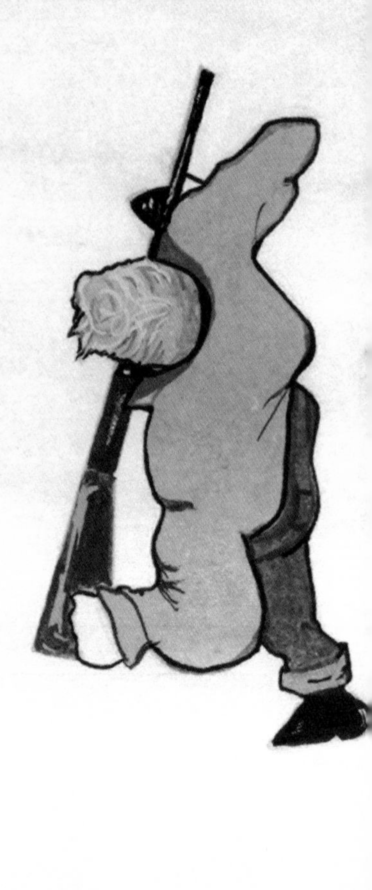

Caril suddenly bolted across the highway towards a passing patrol car, screaming,
"He killed a man!"

Charlie sped off.
The ensuing chase
reached 120 mph.

Surrendering after
shots were fired, he
immediately told the
sheriff that Caril
was completely
innocent.

Caril rode back to Lincoln with the sheriff's wife. She was still wearing a jacket that had belonged to the now-dead Mrs. Ward, and thought it very pretty, despite the bloodstains.

In custody of the state before her trial, Caril's hair was cut short. Her attorney was angry - instead of a cute eighth-grade ponytail she had the look of a much older girl...

She came across as a tough and sullen young woman.

Charles Starkweather maintained that Caril Fugate was not involved in any of the murders for some time, but left graffiti in his holding cell implicating her in two murders.

He also drew their initials together inside a heart.

Charlie was cocky with the press, posing coolly for the cameras.

He was the
most heavily
guarded
prisoner
in state
history.

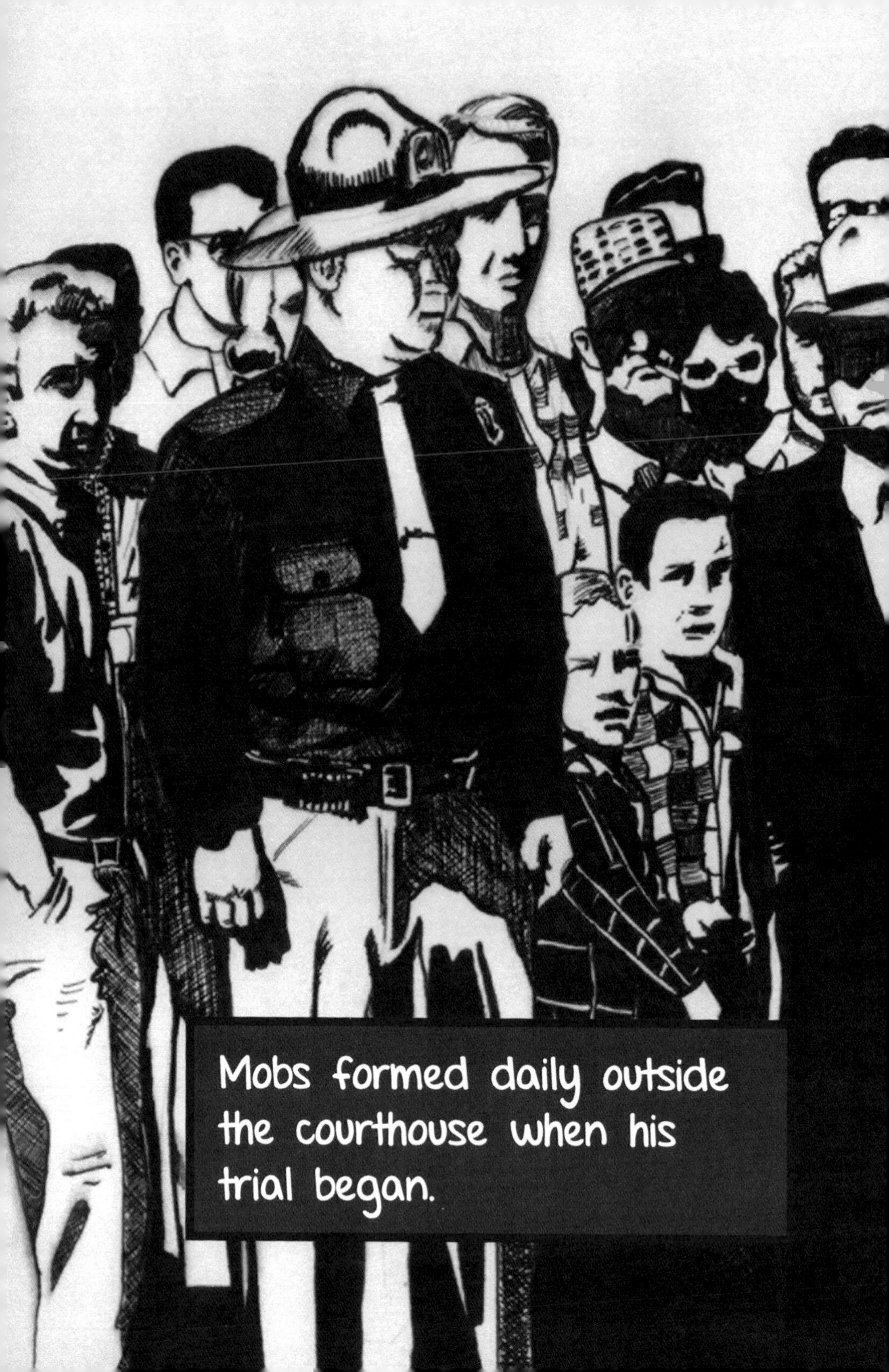
Mobs formed daily outside the courthouse when his trial began.

He remembered his childhood as idyllic: fishing with dad, canning with mom. He and his brothers played cowboys and Indians. He felt loved and happy until he began school at age five.

In jail he wrote about his first school day:

"I began to speak... my voice was smerying faint and cracked, the kids bursted into laughter. I flinch, startle, flaccid, lacking in firmness, then I was completely flabberghast as my words became flat as I started to speak again I sadden they had no regard for my feelings."

"I sat staring out the little door, glaring antagonists, pinioned, thus, strained toward the kids about the room... and it seemed as though I could see my heart before my eyes, turning dark and black with hate of rages, or harlequinade, stripped from... life leaving only naked being - hate."

Although he described his crimes as "self-defense," Charlie and his family opposed an insanity plea.

Caril wrote Charlie a note from custody:
"Chuck, I don't went to sea you, because I might do something I would be sorry for later on."

Then one day Charlie stated that his previous confessions had all been "hogwash," and that Caril was actually his accomplice. He said that in fact she was the most trigger-happy person he had ever seen.

Why should we kill this boy? Let's kill the devil in him!
The defense attorney made an impassioned plea during closing arguments: "Are we going to push this boy down in the electric chair if he has a deranged mind?"
During the trial, Charlie's look was bored, detached. Maintaining a half-smirk, he chewed gum and went to sleep as his confessions were read by the prosecution...

The jury took less than 24hrs to find him guilty of murder in the 1st degree.

Caril had changed her story several times during their extradition, implicating herself.

Many witnesses had seen Caril with Charlie during the ten day spree and testified against her. Her own plea of Not Guilty was unconvincing, full of gaps and changes, her demeanor hostile. Her sentence: Life in Prison.

Caril Ann Fugate was a model prisoner, and continued to claim innocence, but the citizens of Lincoln fought hard against her parole for years.

Charlie Starkweather spent his remaining days writing to his family and composing his memoirs. He enjoyed his notoriety until the end.

Caril was released in 1976. She now resides in Michigan under an assumed name.

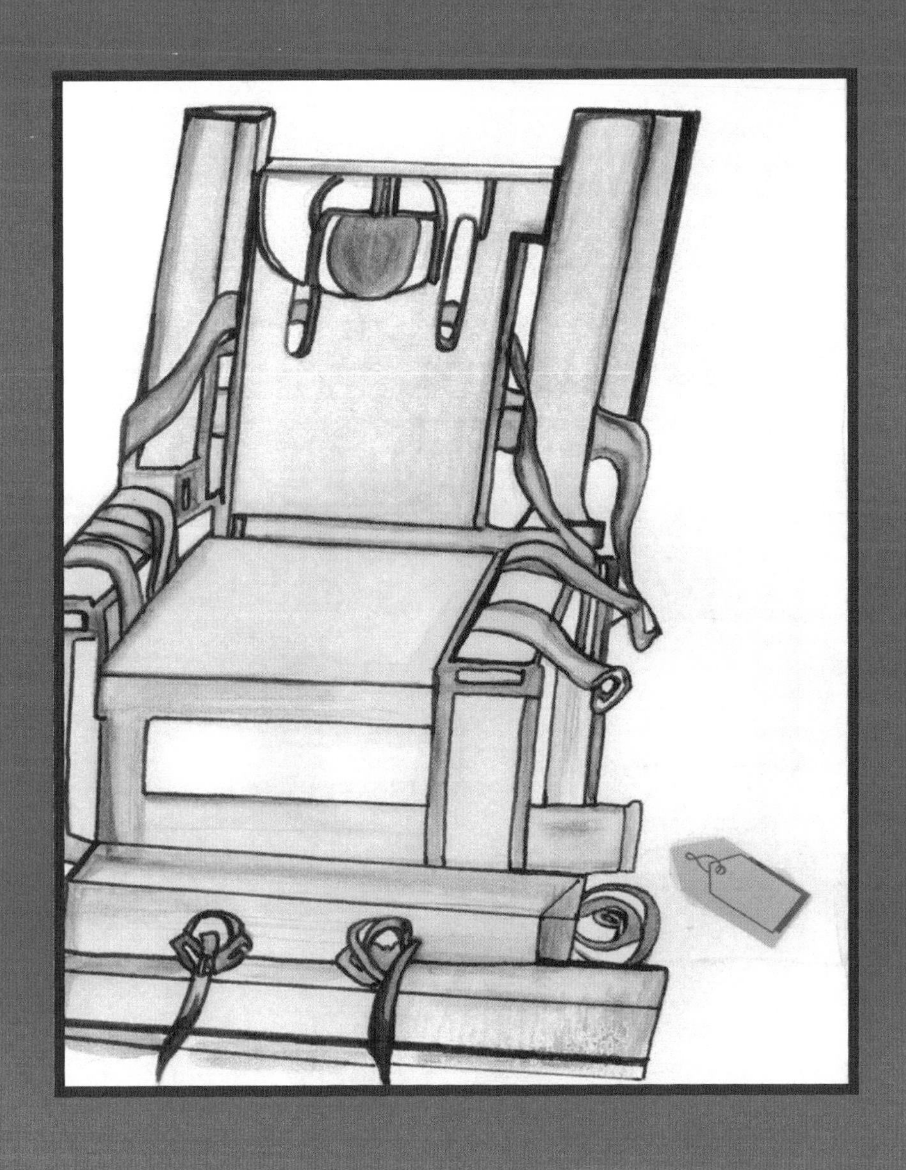

Charlie was the last person to be executed in the state of Nebraska for the next fifty years.

The prison doctor who was appointed to pronounce the execution complete died himself of a heart attack 30 minutes before the scheduled event.

When a new physician arrived at the cell to assist the procedure, Charlie grinned at him, and said his last words: "What's your hurry?"

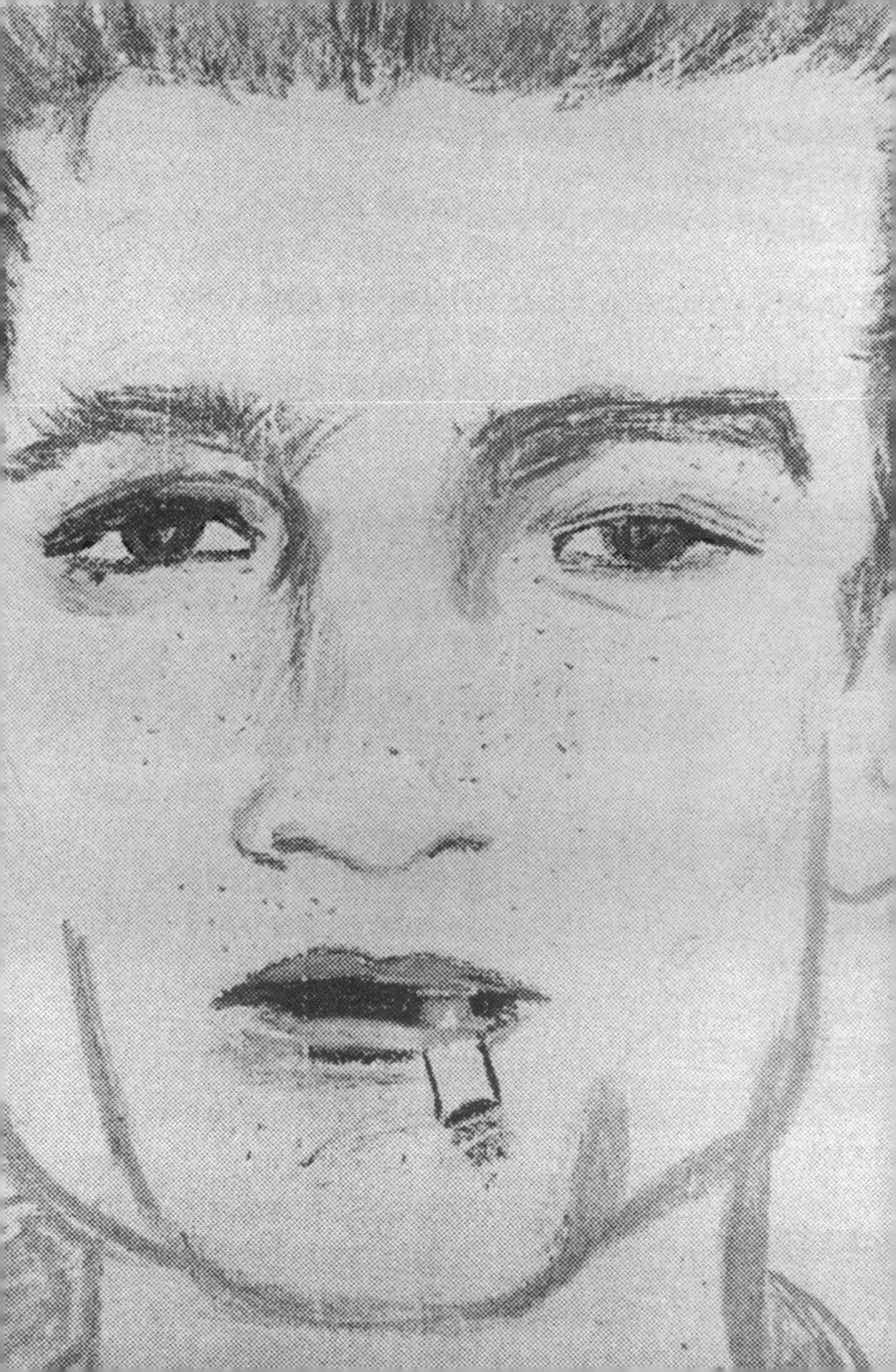

AFTERWORD

Today most people are familiar with the concept of mass murder: a series of killings is committed within a short period of time, without evident provocation. The victims are often random, unlucky strangers. In 1958, the idea of a "killing spree" did not exist.

If 1950s America did not yet have a category in which to place angry young men like Charles Starkweather, they soon would. The antisocial and reckless would be part of the zeitgeist: delinquency and gunplay in *Rebel Without a Cause*, switchblades and frank sexuality in *West Side Story*, teen tragedy songs about dying fiery deaths in crashing cars. Violence was in style.

Charlie Starkweather and Caril Ann Fugate were in many ways much like other young people of their time and place, if from very low-income families. They went to high school, cruised in hot-rods, read comics, went to the movies. Neither was clinically insane, and neither had a police record.

Nevertheless, the media in Lincoln, Nebraska at the time dismissed the murder spree perpetrated by Starkweather as the actions of a disturbed, immature half-wit. His message of anger was largely invalidated by this refusal to examine it.

Today, as then, the residents of Lincoln are conservative and stolid. There is little sense of nostalgia. The town has no reason to look back upon itself because very little changes. It is a community built in the middle of a prairie, the vast plains pressing in. People are at once friendly and distant, as if the vigilance necessary to subjugate the land also subdues emotion.

Because Lincoln is a college town, one might expect it to be progressive. It is not. Students frequent the same establishments their parents and grandparents did. They flock to King's Drive-Thru Burgers, the Stuart Theatre (where Charlie and Caril enjoyed many a black-and-white shoot-'em-up flick) and the Tastee Freeze, not for the sake of kitsch but because they are all still there. There is scant ethnic diversity. Social divisions tend to still be financial. Angry letters appear on the local editorial page demanding harsher laws against "junk cars" that can deplete a neighborhood's status. Born poor, a teenager of his era, it began to seem to me Charlie had little choice but to rebel.

I lived in Lincoln while researching *Short Fuse*. I met many who were connected to the story in some way: a guy whose dad cut Charlie's hair (his father still kept the barbering chair in the basement), the woman who worked the lunch counter where Caril bought burgers and fries the day the farmer was shot, parents who attended school with Charlie and Caril. Some people were related to the victims, some to the prosecution, and some to the jail guards.

One Lincolnite I met attended junior high with Starkweather and recounted escaping his classmate's temper when Charlie complimented him on his Western-style shirt. "I knew what that meant!" he told me. He had immediately stripped off the garment and handed it over as to Charlie as they stood in the schoolyard. Starkweather accepted, offering his own plainer shirt in return. Fifty years later, the man remembered feeling lucky Charlie "didn't beat it off me! He was one tough guy!"

A ninth grade girlfriend recalls a different boy. "He was one of the finest boys I've ever known," she said. "He never swore, drank, smoked, or tried to put his arm around me." Another woman describes the Charlie she knew as "an awfully sweet boy."

Everyone who was alive when the killing spree took place remembers it with surprising freshness. Kids were sent home from school in the middle of the day as reports swirled about an unknown madman on the loose. Two hundred members of the National Guard patrolled the streets in Jeeps mounted with machine guns. Clear in people's minds to this day is the atmosphere of growing horror as some realized they had dated the suspect; that he'd picked up their garbage; that they knew his family.

The longer I was in Lincoln, the more I realized that Starkweather's short-lived reign of terror was in a way the last thing that had any real impact there, and that it was still fairly recent news as far as the town was concerned.

And yet, it was also a taboo subject. The telling of these stories was infuriatingly vague. Again and again, I was subtly rebuffed. Memories were facile. Narration was brief and detached. The topic seemed too distasteful to dwell upon, even among those who purportedly embraced the distasteful. I found skaters, barflies, punks and hipsters to be uniformly circumspect about their unique piece of local lore. The self-proclaimed rebellious subculture proved as conservative as their forbearers in this matter, unwilling to confront the aberration in their collective past.

Was their wariness a deliberate obfuscation, a sly calculation to protect a bona fide Lincoln iconoclast from being exploited? I was, after all, an outsider. I sensed a tightening of the circle. I would never penetrate the secret heart in this fragment of history. The crime scene was closed off.

ABOUT THE AUTHOR

LILI RISTAGNO lives in Portland, Oregon, where she works for the Multnomah County Library. She spent many months in Nebraska researching this book, her first.

The author wishes to thank Anne Marie Distefano, Hillary Johnson, Nancy Rommelmann, Andrew Heithaus, Joe Wilson, John Chandler, Elizabeth and Stuart Campbell, Multnomah County Library employees, the Nebraska State Archives, and the citizens of Lincoln, NE.

Dymaxicon Cult Classics are new editions of books beloved by a handful of hard-core fans—books that deserve more time to grow on readers than conventional publishing schedules tend to allow. We're bringing these dead soldiers back into print, but our new editions are more than "reprints." In many cases, we're re-editing and sometimes restoring the author's original vision (think director's cut).

Lili Ristagno's *Short Fuse* was originally published in a limited edition by the author. The book sold out quickly, and readers who wanted to get their hands on one of the six copies held by the Multnomah County Library had to join a long waiting list.

The Dymaxicon edition gives *Short Fuse* a new layout, and includes new artwork conceived during the editing process.

For more information about Dymaxicon Cult Classics, please visit www.dymaxicon.com.

Made in the USA
Charleston, SC
24 December 2011